Orion Books Ltd

Orion House

5 Upper St Martin's Lane

London WC2H 9EA

First published by Orion 1998

Drawings by Michael Martin

Cover illustrations by Alex Graham

© Associated Newspapers plc 1998

ISBN 0 75281 738 8

Printed and bound in Great Britain
by The Guernsey Press Limited.

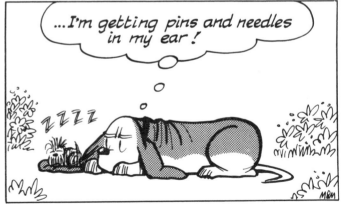

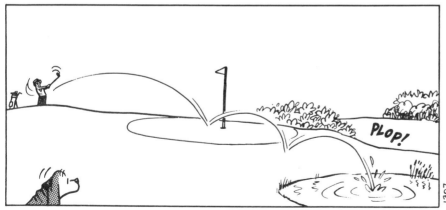

We're on a snatch and grab raid...

Success depends on pluck, bravado, nerves of steel...

...luckily Yorky's got them in abundance!

ZZZZ

1314

Good gracious...

1315

...this place looks like a florist's

It must be her turn to do the church flowers

JIMMY JUST LOVES PLAYING WITH HIS CARS

BRUM BRUM

Hey! Do you mind?

I'm not a humpback bridge, you know!

BRUMMMM

NOT AN EASY JOB, I'M AFRAID— THE GEAR LEVER CARRIER WILL HAVE TO BE REMOVED ALONG WITH THE SELECTOR ROD, THE COUPLING AND THE INTERLOCK PLATE...

GARAGE

...AND THEN WE'LL HAVE TO UNBOLT THE BELL HOUSING, MAKING SURE THE CLUTCH RELEASE COMPONENTS ARE INTACT; YOU'LL NEED A NEW INPUT SHAFT SHIM AND A MAIN-SHAFT ROLLER BEARING...

Would you mind repeating that in English?

I SEE

HE'S BEEN IN THERE FOR AGES

CROWN COURT

...SURELY HIS TRIAL SHOULD BE OVER BY NOW?

Don't worry—he's only doing Jury Service!

THIS PIE IS LOVELY, DEAR — IS IT HOME-MADE?

HOME-MADE? — ...UM... YES, DEAR

Home-made by Mrs Lavender for the W I fete, that is!

She's just treated herself to a new dress — half price in the sale

...but it turns out it's not going to be such a bargain as she thought...

...once she's paid the fine on the wheelclamp!

Did I read that correctly?

They do say a wet nose is a sign of good health...

ATISHOOO!

...but not in his case!

SNIFF SNIFF

The unmistakable signs of Spring — the primroses are blooming...

...the trees are burgeoning forth — there's the sound of a distant cuckoo

...and the grunting and groaning from the vegetable patch

UH—

BYE-BYE, DEAR, SO NICE TO SEE YOU AGAIN

MY, MY, SHE LOOKS RATHER FRUMPY THESE DAYS, AND HASN'T SHE PUT ON SOME WEIGHT?

YES

AND SHE'S YOUNGER THAN YOU, ISN'T SHE?

YES

It's made her day bumping into Felicity after all these years!